X-MEN ANNUAL 2006

G000230369

£6.99

GREAT BRITAIN

BISHOP, MARVEL GIRL & CANNONBALL ARE ON ROUTE TO BRADDOCK MANOR*

♪ "IN THE WHITE ROOM, WITH BLACK CURTAINS, AT THE STATION..." ♪

WHAT'S THAT, RACHEL?

ONE OF MY MOM'S FAVORITE SONGS.

ME, I PREFER PSYCHIC FRACTAL GEOMANCERS.

?

CHICAGO BAND. PUNK PARTICLE PHYSICISTS.

TOTALLY CLASSIC.

HEY, SAM, APROPOS OF NOTHING SPECIAL--

--WHEN DO YOU GUTHRIES GET TO FORM YOUR OWN TEAM OF X-MEN?

YEAH! HOW MANY OF YOU ARE ACTIVE MUTANTS?

WELL, I GOT A BROTHER WITH WINGS, CAN YOU BELIEVE IT?

NOT TO MENTION YOUR TWO SISTERS. HOW'S YOUR MOM FEEL WITH ALL THAT?

SHE ENROLLED JAY AT THE INSTITUTE, AND OF COURSE HE TOTALLY HATES IT. WHICH MEANS HE HATES ME.

HE'LL GET OVER IT.

OH MAN, YOU DO NOT WANT TO KNOW HOW MAMA REACTED WHEN SHE SAW US ON TV.

*HOME OF CAPTAIN BRITAIN

WHEN SHE CALLED, I FELT LIKE A KID AGAIN.

ON MY WAY OUT TO THE WOODSHED.

KIND'A LIKE HOW I FEEL NOW...

...I'M SO NERVOUS COMING BACK HERE AFTER ALL THIS TIME.

5

9

10

11

IT ADJUSTS THE POLYMER MATRIX OF ITS SHELL TO RESIST THE TARGET'S MAXIMUM *HEAT* COEFFICIENT.

I LOVE YOU, MAMA.

TARGET MANIPULATES KINETIC ENERGIES TO GENERATE MOTIVE POWER AND AN ENVELOPE OF *PROTECTION.*

PAIGE-- YOU'LL BE THE *OLDEST* NOW.

LOOK AFTER *JAY* AN' *MELODY,* SIS. MAKE ME PROUD!

BEING DYNAMIC, THE SYSTEM IS INHERENTLY *UNSTABLE.*

SHLUKT!

AND THEREBY *VULNERABLE.*

THIS OBJECT IS... *INTRIGUING.*

IT REPRESENTS A *LOCUS* OF EXTRAORDINARY CYBERNETIC POWER.

⊗THE XAVIER INSTITUTE FOR HIGHER LEARNING

INSIDE *SAGE'S* CARRIAGE HOUSE.

IT WILL FOLLOW THE NETWORK BACK TO ITS *SOURCE.*

SAM?!

AND IF IT PROVES *USEFUL* IN THE FULFILLMENT OF ITS PRIME DIRECTIVE...

...*ASSIMILATE* IT.

CONTINUED
ON PAGE 18

15

X-MEN PROFILE...

NAME: ORORO MUNROE
X-MEN DESIGNATE:

STORM!

BACKGROUND: Ororo was raised in Cairo, Egypt. Disastrously, her parents were killed in an explosion when she was a child and she, herself, was buried under rubble.

Ororo was found and raised by master thief Achmed el-Gibar and she became his star pupil. At the age of twelve Ororo left Egypt for Africa. Due to her newly manifested mutant weather powers, she was venerated by a local tribe as a goddess.

Professor X persuaded her to join the X-Men and she has been a stalwart member ever since, even acting as second team leader.

MUTANT POWERS: Weather Control. Storm has total control over weather formations allowing her to fly, summon hurricanes, blizzards, rain storms as well as lightning with which to blast her opponents.

>>

STRENGTH:
AGILITY:
ENDURANCE:
INTELLIGENCE:
COMBAT SKILL:
POWER:

X-MEN PROFILE...

NAME: SAMUEL 'SAM' GUTHERIE
X-MEN DESIGNATE:

CANNONBALL!

BACKGROUND: Sam is the eldest son of a Kentucky coal mining family. Sam's mutant powers first manifested themselves when he and a co-worker were buried when the mine roof collapsed and allowed Sam to blast them free.

Unfortunately, this brought Sam to the attention of Donald Pierce (of the nefarious Hellfire Club) who recruited the young mutant to kill Professor X's youngest students, the New Mutants.

Sam refused and rescued the New Mutants. In gratitude, Professor X enrolled Sam in his School for Gifted Youngsters, where he served as team leader of the New Mutants. Sam recently graduated to the X-Men.

MUTANT POWERS: Thermo-chemical energy generation. Cannonball is capable of surrounding himself in an explosive forcefield of energy that turns him into a human rocket and can fly at approxiamately 150 mph. In addition, the forcefield protects him from harm, making him nearly invulnerable. Sam can focus his energy field and use it to project powerful blasts of energy from his hands. >>>>>>>>>>>>>>

STRENGTH:
AGILITY:
ENDURANCE:
INTELLIGENCE:
COMBAT SKILL:
POWER:

X-MEN PROFILE.. SAGE!

NAME: TESSA
X-MEN DESIGNATE:

BACKGROUND: Professor Xavier recruited Tessa during the formative days of the X-Men. Unlike her fellow X-Men however, Tessa was sent to spy on the villainous Hellfire Club and, specifically, its leader Sebastian Shaw – who she served as his personal assistant.

After years of working for Shaw, Tessa broke her cover and joined the X-Men as an advisor and trainer. Although usually providing critical advice from the X-Mansion, Sage is a capable field operative.

MUTANT POWERS: Genetic Perception and Enhancement, Telepathy, Cyberpath. Sage has the unique ability to detect and unlock the mutant ability within others, unleashing their full potential, as well as being an accomplished telepath. In addition, Sage has advanced mental capabilities allowing her total assimilation and recall of information making her the equivalent of a human computer. >>>>>>

STRENGTH:
AGILITY:
ENDURANCE:
INTELLIGENCE:
COMBAT SKILL:
POWER:

X-MEN PROFILE... BISHOP!

NAME: BISHOP   **X-MEN DESIGNATE:**

BACKGROUND: Bishop was born in an alternative future time-line where the mutant hunting robots, the Sentinels, had destroyed the X-Men and assumed control of the Earth. The young Bishop was raised in a 'Mutant Relocation Camp', where he received his identifying 'M' tattoo over his right eye, and grew up hearing tales of the legendary mutant heroes the X-Men. Eventually, the oppressed humans and mutants joined forces and overthrew the Sentinels.

After the rebellion and in order to effectively police mutants, the XSE (Xavier Security Enforcers) were formed. Bishop enrolled and proved to be a successful officer. When the mutant criminal Trevor Fitzroy, escaped prison and fled back in time to the present day, Bishop pursued and defeated him.

Xavier and the X-Men found Bishop and inducted him into the team. Feeling honoured to serve among the heroes he had idolized since childhood, Bishop has proven his worth as an X-Man time and again.

MUTANT POWERS: Energy Absorption. Bishop is capable of absorbing practically any form of energy fired at him and then redirecting the energy as powerful blasts from his hands.
>>>>>>>>>>>>>>>>>>>>>>>>>>

STRENGTH:
AGILITY:
ENDURANCE:
INTELLIGENCE:
COMBAT SKILL:
POWER:

21

30

CONTINUED ON PAGE 35

31

10 THINGS YOU NEVER KNEW ABOUT... THE X-MEN!

Think you're an X-Men *Xpert*? You will be once you've read these 10 amazing X-facts about Marvel's mutants!

MULTIPLE MUTANTS!

1 Over 50 mutants have joined the ranks of the X-Men since the group was first formed!

PHOENIX RISING!

2 After dying in a space shuttle crash, Jean Grey was resurrected by a mystical force known as the Phoenix. She can now use the power of the Phoenix to boost her telepathic and telekinetic powers to incredible levels!

3 FROM MAN TO BEAST!

Believe it or not, this is how the Beast looked when he first joined the X-Men! It wasn't until later, when he drank an experimental serum which he hoped would cure his mutant genes, that he turned into the blue-furred Beast we all know and love.

More recently his appearance has changed once again and he has now started to resemble a giant cat!

GALACTIC GADGETS!

4 Professor X has a very close relationship with Empress Lilandra, the head of the alien Shi'ar Empire. Because of this the X-Men's mansion has been upgraded to incorporate large amounts of hi-tech alien technology such as super efficient fusion generators and robotic caretakers!

FUTURE IMPERFECT!

Professor Xavier's crazed son Legion once went back in time and killed his father! This caused the future to change and a whole new reality to appear which became known as the *Age of Apocalypse.*

In this reality Apocalypse and the Sentinels had taken over America, and the X-Men were now a rag-tag band of freedom fighters led by none other than Magneto!

5

ORIGIN...

6

Wolverine's real name is actually James Howlett, not Logan. He was born over 150 years ago to a wealthy family of landowners but was forced to leave after his mutant powers manifested. However, Wolverine still has no memory of his early life.

7

CREATURE COMFORTS!

Even the X-Men's pets are pretty kooky! Kitty Pryde, better known as Shadowcat, has a miniature pet dragon called Lockheed!

8

MINI MARVELS!

An intergalactic villain called Mojo once created a pint-sized version of the X-Men known as the X-Babies!

9

CALM BEFORE THE STORM!

Although Professor X did not invite Storm to join the X-Men until she was much older, he first met her in Egypt when she was only six years old. She was living on the streets at the time and tried to steal the professor's wallet.

10

WHAT'S IN A NAME...

When it was first printed, the X-Men comic was originally going to be called 'The Mutants.' However the name was changed as the writers were worried that nobody would know what a mutant was!

>>COLOUR
X-TREME! >>>>>>>>>>>>>>

Grab your pens and add some colour so
the X-Men can defeat The Fury in style!

AGAINST SOME ADVERSARIES, THEY DARE NOT SHOW THE SLIGHTEST *MERCY.*

NO!

I--WILL *NOT*--DO THIS!

STORM'S ELECTROMAGNETIC PULSE CRIPPLED THE CYBORG NANITES INFECTING SAGE, AND THE CYBER-GLASSES FROM WHICH THEY WERE CREATED...

I WILL BE *NO ONE'S SLAVE!*

...BUT SAGE CAN FEEL THEM ADAPTING.

SHE HAS BUT A MOMENT TO ACT. AND ONLY THIS ONE CHANCE.

SHE WAS BORN WITH AN INDOMITABLE WILL. CHARLES XAVIER TAUGHT HER THAT THE MIND IS OF THE *BODY*, THE *BODY* OF THE *MIND*.

PROPERLY FOCUSED, HER CAPABILITIES ARE EXTRAORDINARY.

AND HE STILL CONSIDERS SAGE VERY MUCH A WORK IN PROGRESS.

FOR NOW, THOUGH, SHE'S GRATEFUL FOR WHAT SHE'S LEARNED.

SAGE?

SAGE?

YOU CAN ALL *STAND DOWN*.

I AM *MYSELF* AGAIN.

BY *FOCUSED* APPLICATION OF MY WILL, I TREATED THE CYBORG ELEMENTS LIKE ANY BIOLOGICAL *VIRUS*.

AND *PURGED* THEM!

AS FOR THE CREATURE *RESPONSIBLE*--

--IT CALLS ITSELF *THE FURY!*

IT DOESN'T KNOW THE *MEANING* OF THE WORD.

37

CONTINUED ON PAGE 41

X-MEN PROFILE...

NAME: KURT WAGNER
X-MEN DESIGNATE:

NIGHTCRAWLER!

BACKGROUND: As a baby, Kurt Wagner was abandoned by his mother, the mutant terrorist Mystique, and raised by the performers of a Bavarian travelling circus. Kurt quickly revealed a natural talent for acrobatics and became a star attraction. As a teenager, Kurt left the circus and resurfaced in the small German town of Winzeldorf. Disastrously, the townspeople, alarmed at the Kurt's appearance, blamed him for a series of recent murders and were about to lynch the hapless mutant when Professor X rescued him. In return Kurt accepted Xavier's offer of a place on his new team of X-Men.

MUTANT POWERS: Teleportation, Wall-crawling, Prehensile tale. Nightcrawler can teleport himself distances of up to 2 miles. In addition, he can cling to nearly any surface and is blessed with incredible natural agility that is enhanced by his prehensile tale.

NIGHTCRAWLER uses a holographic Image Inducer to hide his mutant appearance. >>>>>>>

STRENGTH:
AGILITY:
ENDURANCE:
INTELLIGENCE:
COMBAT SKILL:
POWER:

X-MEN PROFILE...

NAME: RACHEL SUMMERS

X-MEN DESIGNATE:

MARVEL GIRL!

STRENGTH:
AGILITY:
ENDURANCE:
INTELLIGENCE:
COMBAT SKILL:
POWER:

BACKGROUND: Rachel is the daughter of Scott Summers (Cyclops) and Jean Grey (Phoenix, the original Marvel Girl) from an alternate future. Disastrously in this nightmarish future, the Sentinels destroyed all of Rachel's family and friends. Rachel eventually escaped into the past where she joined the present day X-Men.

Soon after, Rachel found that she could manifest the Phoenix Force, the same as her mother, although currently, she only has a limited access to this phenomenal power.

MUTANT POWERS:
Telekinisis, Telepathy. Phoenix Force. Marvel Girl's telekinisis allows her to manipulate objects with the power of her mind, create force fields, fly at speeds of up to 150 mph and blast opponents with bolts of kinetic energy. Her telepathy allows Marvel Girl to read minds, as well as blast them with psionic bolts. When Marvel Girl uses the power of the Phoenix Force it greatly enhances her powers.

WOLVERINE!

X-MEN PROFILE...

NAME: JAMES HOWLETT, CURRENTLY KNOWN AS LOGAN
X-MEN DESIGNATE:

STRENGTH:		
AGILITY:		
ENDURANCE:		
INTELLIGENCE:		
COMBAT SKILL:		
POWER:		

BACKGROUND: Little is known of Logan's origin and due to his power of regeneration it is nearly impossible to determine his true age. What is known is that he fought during World War II and many years later became a CIA 'Black Ops' agent. Logan then volunteered for the Weapon X programme, a top secret US government operation designed to create super soldiers. During an extremely painful operation, the scientists of Weapon X laced Logan's skeleton with the indestructible metal, adamantium.

In order to control Logan they erased his memories, however, his animal nature was too strong and he escaped. James and Heather Hudson of the Canadian super team Alpha Flight, found him and nursed him back to sanity. He later joined Canada's Department H where he was code-named Wolverine.

It was whilst at Department H that Wolverine was approached by Professor X, who recruited him for the X-Men. Logan is a superb fighter and trained in many forms of martial arts. In combat however, he has a tendency of entering into a animalistic rage where he becomes a danger to not just his foes, but friends as well.

MUTANT POWERS: Adamantium Skeleton, Claws, Healing Factor, Enhanced Senses. Wolverine's skeleton is laced with adamantium, the strongest metal known to man and virtually indestructible, making his bones unbreakable. In addition, he is equipped with three retractable claws on each hand, which can cut through almost anything.

Wolverine also possesses a healing factor. This ability allows him to regenerate from incredible injuries that would kill a normal man, including bullet wounds and being set on fire. His healing factor also makes him nearly immune to all poisons and diseases. In addition, Wolverine's senses of smell and hearing are superhumanly acute allowing him to track people just by their scent or detect a hidden assassin by their heartbeat.

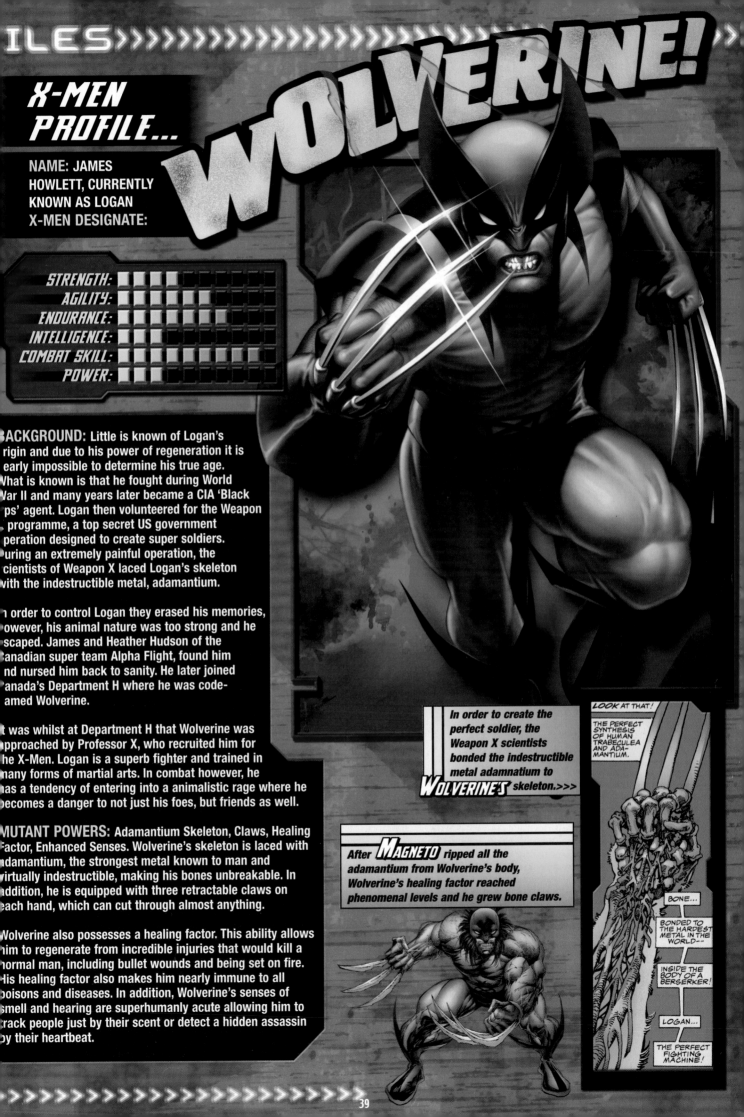

In order to create the perfect soldier, the Weapon X scientists bonded the indestructible metal adamantium to WOLVERINE'S skeleton.≫≫

After MAGNETO ripped all the adamantium from Wolverine's body, Wolverine's healing factor reached phenomenal levels and he grew bone claws.

LOOK AT THAT!
THE PERFECT SYNTHESIS OF HUMAN TRABECULEA AND ADA-MANTIUM.

BONE...

BONDED TO THE HARDEST METAL IN THE WORLD--

INSIDE THE BODY OF A BERSERKER!

LOGAN...

THE PERFECT FIGHTING MACHINE!

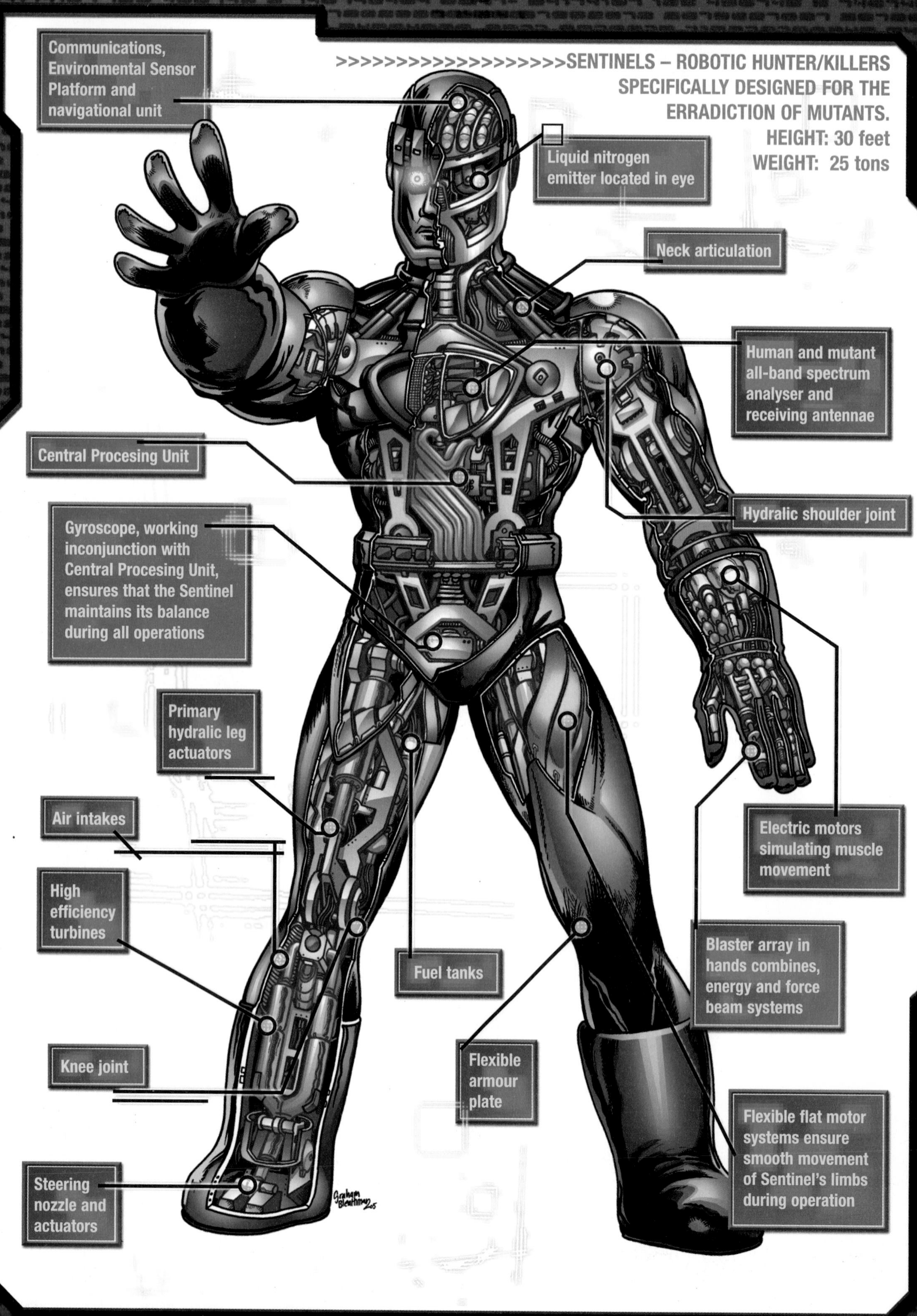

Communications, Environmental Sensor Platform and navigational unit

>>>>>>>>>>>>>>>>>>>SENTINELS – ROBOTIC HUNTER/KILLERS SPECIFICALLY DESIGNED FOR THE ERRADICTION OF MUTANTS.
HEIGHT: 30 feet
WEIGHT: 25 tons

Liquid nitrogen emitter located in eye

Neck articulation

Human and mutant all-band spectrum analyser and receiving antennae

Central Procesing Unit

Hydralic shoulder joint

Gyroscope, working inconjunction with Central Procesing Unit, ensures that the Sentinel maintains its balance during all operations

Primary hydralic leg actuators

Air intakes

Electric motors simulating muscle movement

High efficiency turbines

Fuel tanks

Blaster array in hands combines, energy and force beam systems

Knee joint

Flexible armour plate

Flexible flat motor systems ensure smooth movement of Sentinel's limbs during operation

Steering nozzle and actuators

IT TRIES FOCUSED PLASMA BEAMS, MESON CUTTERS, SONIC-PULSE CANNONS, ROUNDS OF DEPLETED NEUTRONIUM...

...IT TRIES RAW STRENGTH AND SPEED AND WHAT PASSES IN ITS MATRIX FOR *GUILE.*

YET THE TARGET *SURVIVES.*

VRAAAMM!

AS IT *ADAPTS* TO THE TARGET, THE TARGET, THOUGH WOUNDED, ADAPTS AS WELL.

IF IT HAD THE CAPABILITY FOR EMOTION, IT WOULD FIND THIS *ANNOYING.*

INSTEAD IT *INCREASES* ITS CAPABILITIES.

EVEN *MUTANT* PHYSIOLOGY HAS *LIMITS.*

IT DOES *NOT.*

THE *TARGET* MAY BE *SMARTER,* BUT IN THE END, HE WILL *PERISH.*

LIKE *ALL* BEFORE HIM.

43

44

46

48

CONTINUED ON PAGE 52

SAGE'S CYBER CONUNDRUMS

The Fury has hacked into the X-Mansion's computer network. Sage needs your help to de-bug the system and erradicate the virus.

```
S T O R M W F G H J I K
A Q E Z D O A Q S D C J
N I G H T C R A W L E R
A A A B I S H O P A M X
A V H K G A A G Q A A A
D A R A A G A R A A N B
A W O L V E R I N E A A
G A G A E R F B J N W A
K A U A A W A A W O A F
A A E W O M A I C A E A
C A N N O N B A L L A K
```

■ The Fury has hidden 8 of the X-Men's identities within the word grid above. Can you locate these X-men? Nightcrawler, Rogue, Sage, Ice Man, Cannonball, Wolverine, Bishop and Storm

QUERY... ÌÈÁÙÇ X–MEN IDENTIFICATION Ì X-MEN IDENTIFICATION Ì ÌÓØ~ π

■ The Fury has scrambled the mansion's electronic visual recognition systems.

Can you identify the four X-Men who appear in the image above?

SINISTER CYBER SPACE!

■ Sage needs your help to navigate her probe through the X-Men's infected computer systems and purge them of the Fury's influence!

Can you find the safest path through cyberspace to the main computer avoiding the Fury's dangerous computer viruses?!

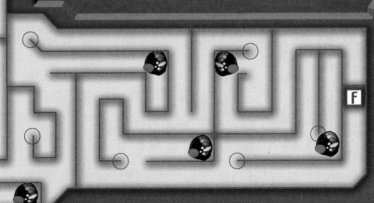

Answers on page 63.

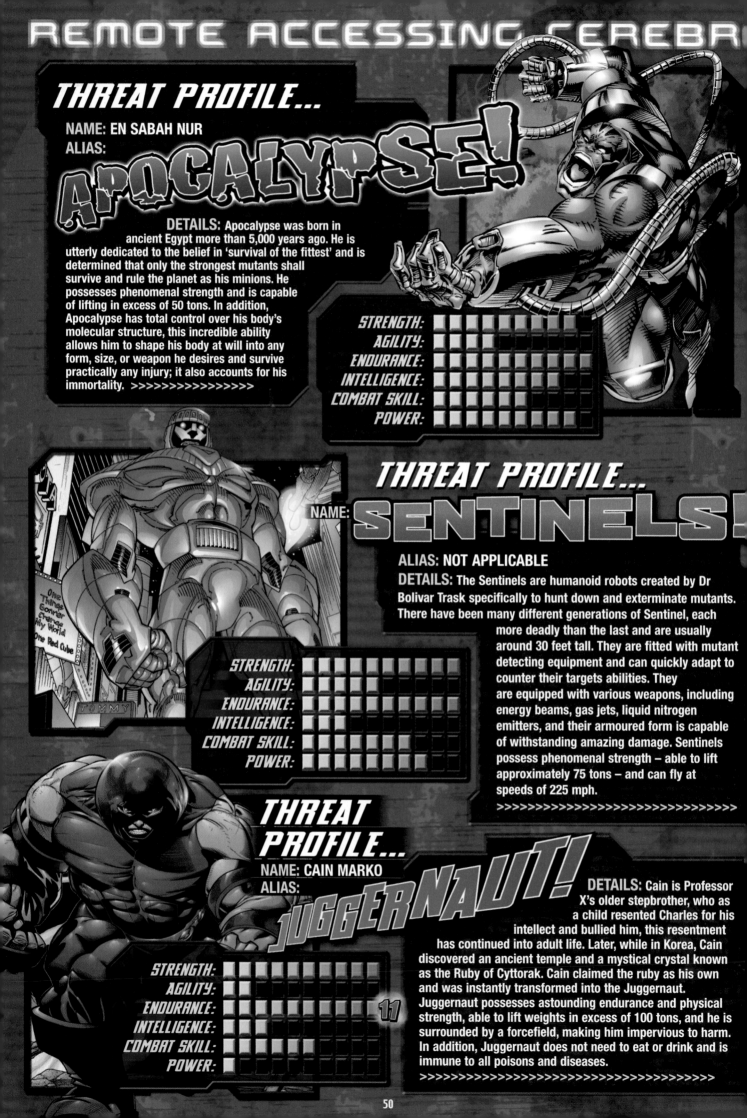

THREAT PROFILE...

NAME: EN SABAH NUR
ALIAS:

APOCALYPSE!

DETAILS: Apocalypse was born in ancient Egypt more than 5,000 years ago. He is utterly dedicated to the belief in 'survival of the fittest' and is determined that only the strongest mutants shall survive and rule the planet as his minions. He possesses phenomenal strength and is capable of lifting in excess of 50 tons. In addition, Apocalypse has total control over his body's molecular structure, this incredible ability allows him to shape his body at will into any form, size, or weapon he desires and survive practically any injury; it also accounts for his immortality. >>>>>>>>>>>>>>>>

STRENGTH:
AGILITY:
ENDURANCE:
INTELLIGENCE:
COMBAT SKILL:
POWER:

THREAT PROFILE...

NAME: SENTINELS!

ALIAS: NOT APPLICABLE

DETAILS: The Sentinels are humanoid robots created by Dr Bolivar Trask specifically to hunt down and exterminate mutants. There have been many different generations of Sentinel, each more deadly than the last and are usually around 30 feet tall. They are fitted with mutant detecting equipment and can quickly adapt to counter their targets abilities. They are equipped with various weapons, including energy beams, gas jets, liquid nitrogen emitters, and their armoured form is capable of withstanding amazing damage. Sentinels possess phenomenal strength – able to lift approximately 75 tons – and can fly at speeds of 225 mph.
>>>>>>>>>>>>>>>>>>>>>>>>>>>>>>

STRENGTH:
AGILITY:
ENDURANCE:
INTELLIGENCE:
COMBAT SKILL:
POWER:

THREAT PROFILE...

NAME: CAIN MARKO
ALIAS:

JUGGERNAUT!

DETAILS: Cain is Professor X's older stepbrother, who as a child resented Charles for his intellect and bullied him, this resentment has continued into adult life. Later, while in Korea, Cain discovered an ancient temple and a mystical crystal known as the Ruby of Cyttorak. Cain claimed the ruby as his own and was instantly transformed into the Juggernaut. Juggernaut possesses astounding endurance and physical strength, able to lift weights in excess of 100 tons, and he is surrounded by a forcefield, making him impervious to harm. In addition, Juggernaut does not need to eat or drink and is immune to all poisons and diseases.
>>>>>>>>>>>>>>>>>>>>>>>>>>>>>>>

STRENGTH:
AGILITY:
ENDURANCE:
INTELLIGENCE:
COMBAT SKILL:
POWER:

11

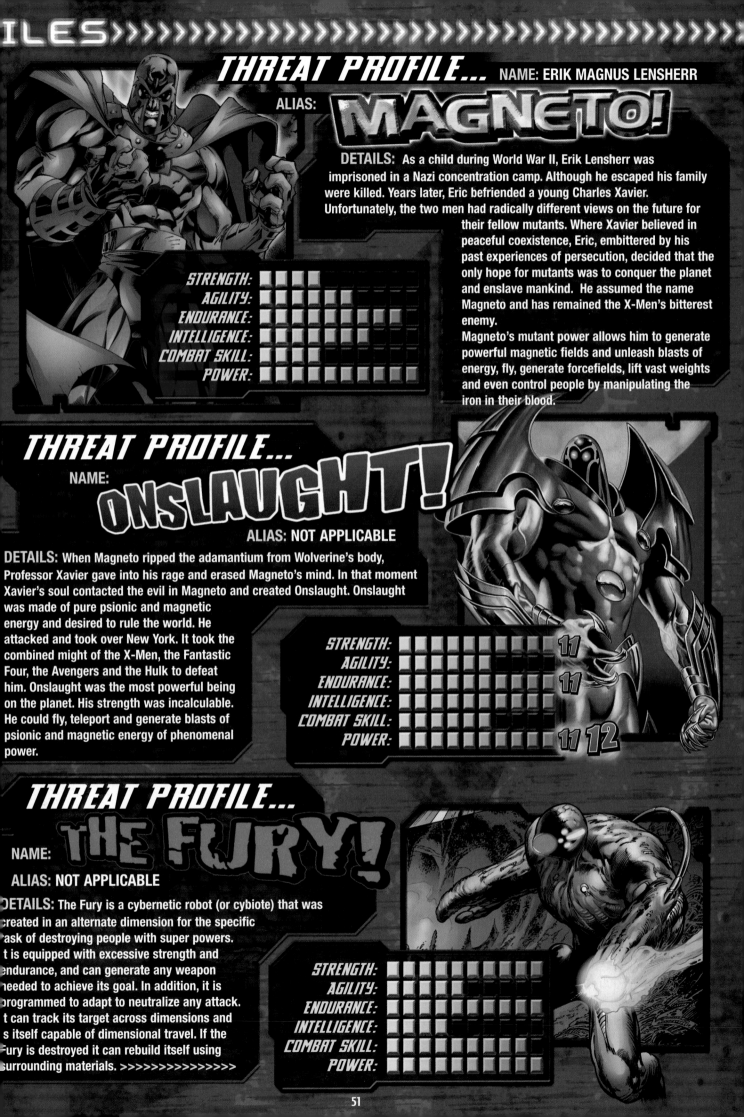

THREAT PROFILE... NAME: ERIK MAGNUS LENSHERR

ALIAS: MAGNETO!

DETAILS: As a child during World War II, Erik Lensherr was imprisoned in a Nazi concentration camp. Although he escaped his family were killed. Years later, Eric befriended a young Charles Xavier. Unfortunately, the two men had radically different views on the future for their fellow mutants. Where Xavier believed in peaceful coexistence, Eric, embittered by his past experiences of persecution, decided that the only hope for mutants was to conquer the planet and enslave mankind. He assumed the name Magneto and has remained the X-Men's bitterest enemy.

Magneto's mutant power allows him to generate powerful magnetic fields and unleash blasts of energy, fly, generate forcefields, lift vast weights and even control people by manipulating the iron in their blood.

STRENGTH:
AGILITY:
ENDURANCE:
INTELLIGENCE:
COMBAT SKILL:
POWER:

THREAT PROFILE...

NAME: ONSLAUGHT!

ALIAS: NOT APPLICABLE

DETAILS: When Magneto ripped the adamantium from Wolverine's body, Professor Xavier gave into his rage and erased Magneto's mind. In that moment Xavier's soul contacted the evil in Magneto and created Onslaught. Onslaught was made of pure psionic and magnetic energy and desired to rule the world. He attacked and took over New York. It took the combined might of the X-Men, the Fantastic Four, the Avengers and the Hulk to defeat him. Onslaught was the most powerful being on the planet. His strength was incalculable. He could fly, teleport and generate blasts of psionic and magnetic energy of phenomenal power.

STRENGTH:
AGILITY: 11
ENDURANCE: 11
INTELLIGENCE:
COMBAT SKILL:
POWER: 11 12

THREAT PROFILE...

NAME: THE FURY!

ALIAS: NOT APPLICABLE

DETAILS: The Fury is a cybernetic robot (or cybiote) that was created in an alternate dimension for the specific task of destroying people with super powers. It is equipped with excessive strength and endurance, and can generate any weapon needed to achieve its goal. In addition, it is programmed to adapt to neutralize any attack. It can track its target across dimensions and is itself capable of dimensional travel. If the Fury is destroyed it can rebuild itself using surrounding materials. >>>>>>>>>>>>>>>>

STRENGTH:
AGILITY:
ENDURANCE:
INTELLIGENCE:
COMBAT SKILL:
POWER:

IT RESPONDS TO PERCEIVED THREATS.

...BY A MERE WOMAN?

PROCESSING VISUAL IMAGERY TO ESTABLISH IDENTITY...

FI01010//:001_ 10F$%^

GLOBAL 101_101 SYSTEM REBOOT

WHAT THREAT IS POSED...

PROXIMITY SENSORS DETECT CONTACT. POSTURE: NON-HOSTILE. DANGER TO UNIT: MINIMAL

WARNING WARNING WARNING!

FOR ALL ITS POWER, THE FURY REALLY IS QUITE STUPID.

IT CANNOT INVENT STRATEGY, IT MERELY FOLLOWS ITS PROGRAMMING.

TOO LATE!

IT ISN'T ALWAYS A MATTER OF RAW STRENGTH.

IT'S KNOWING WHEN AND WHERE TO STRIKE...

...AND PRECISELY WHAT TO AIM FOR!

53

THESE ARE CLUSTER MUNITIONS, A BIG BOMB MADE UP OF LOTS OF LITTLE BOMBS.

EACH BOMBLET IS A PULSE GENERATOR, PRODUCING FLAT PLANES OF ENERGY THAT SEVER THE LINES OF FORCE BINDING TOGETHER MATTER.

INSTANT DISINTEGRATION, DOWN TO THE SUBATOMIC LEVEL.

WHATEVER THEY CUT ESSENTIALLY CEASES TO EXIST.

MY-- GOD!

WHERE'D THAT COME FROM?

SAGE FOUND THEM IN THE X-MEN ARSENAL.

I'M SORRY, GUYS, IT CAN'T BE THIS EASY.

THE CREATURE'S ADAPTED TO EVERYTHING WE TRIED.

THAT'S WHY I TOOK THIS.

WHICH IS?

ITS CORE PROCESSING UNIT.

AS WE SPEAK, IT'S *GROWING* A NEW ONE.

BUT FOR THE FIRST TIME, IT IS *VULNERABLE.*

LIMITED TO ITS MOST *BASIC* FUNCTIONS.

STRAP ON, ELF.

NO WAY DO I LOOK THIS SILLY *SOLO.*

I THINK IT'S *CUTE.*

YOU *THINK* TOO FLAMIN' MUCH!

YO, BISHOP, HOW'S YOUR *AIM?*

YOU'LL HAVE ABOUT A *SPLIT-SECOND* TO HIT THE TARGET *PERFECTLY* AND PULL THEM CLEAR.

OR THEY'LL BE *DEAD.*

SO HAVE KURT *TELEPORT.*

HE'S USED THAT BEFORE, HE'LL USE IT GOING IN.

THE *FURY* WILL NOTE THE EVENT AND PREPARE *COUNTER-MEASURES.*

IT'S LIMITED, LUCAS, BUT STILL INCREDIBLY *DANGEROUS.*

I WON'T LET YOU DOWN.

WE'RE COUNTIN' ON IT.

56

YANK!

THE FURY'S REACTION IS INSTINCTIVE AND VIRTUALLY INSTANTANEOUS, TO EXPEL THE FOREIGN.

BUT BEFORE IT CAN DO SO...

MY TURN.

...RACHEL GREY REACHES OUT WITH THE POWER OF HER MIND...

...HER ABILITY TO MANIPULATE MATTER WITH THE FORCE OF THOUGHT.

TO RACHEL, THE SUBSTANCE OF THE FURY IS QUICKSILVER. HER TELEKINESIS CAN'T MAKE CONTACT.

THE BOX SERVES AS HER ANCHOR POINT.

SHE TAKES HOLD AND BEGINS TO SQUEEZE...

...COMPRESSING ITS MOLECULAR STRUCTURE UNTIL IT FORMS A MICRO-SINGULARITY.

JUST LIKE THAT, SHE BUILDS HER OWN BLACK HOLE...

...CREATING A GRAVITY WELL OF SUCH UNIMAGINABLE AND IRRESISTIBLE FORCE THAT NOT EVEN LIGHT CAN ESCAPE.

AT THE SAME TIME, ALL PHYSICAL REALITIES IN THE IMMEDIATE VICINITY ARE WARPED BEYOND RECOGNITION. BOTH SPACE AND TIME LOSE COHERENCE.

THE FURY'S BREAKING UP! WE'RE WINNING.

MAYBE, STORM.

MAYBE NOT.

IT IS IN A RACE WITH ITS OWN ANNIHILATION.

CREATING LOCALIZED TACHYON SHUNTS TO BLEED OFF THE COSMIC SUCTION...

WEAVING POLYMER WHIPS TO SHATTER THE CONTAINMENT VESSEL THAT CAUSES THIS CHAOS...

INCREASING ITS OVERALL DENSITY BEYOND THE POINT WHERE IT CAN BE AFFECTED BY THE SINGULARITY...

IT'S ADAPTING.

I'M TRYING MY BEST!

BUT--I DON'T HAVE THE STRENGTH!

THIS IS NICE.

RACHEL?

G'WAY! LEMME ALONE! I WANT TO STAY!

AREN'T *YOU* JUST FULL OF *SURPRISES*.

HOW DO YOU *FEEL?*

I ACHE.

WE *ALL* ACHE.

BUT THAT CERTAINLY BEATS THE *ALTERNATIVE.*

KURT!

YOU'RE *ALL RIGHT!* YOU'RE *ALIVE!*

OF *COURSE!* WEREN'T YOU PAYING *ATTENTION?*

THANKS TO *MARVEL GIRL...*

...WE *WON!*

THE END